KV-448-104

STAGE
3
BOOK 1

SCREAM

John Townsend

Riverside Primary School

Janeway Street
SE16 4PS
Telephone 020 7237 3227 • Facsimile 020 7237 0047

RISING STARS

Gran Val came out of the lift and screamed. A hand was by her feet. It was Tasha's.

As Gran Val went into her flat, the cat's face peeped out. The cat began to eat the meat from the tray.

The stray cat played with the toy rat. Then it ran off with it.

At bedtime, Jack went to get the toy rat.

Gran hasn't seen this yet. I'll take it in and put it on her bed.

1. Why did Gran Val scream?

2. What was Tasha doing?

3. Why was Gran Val unhappy about leaving out cat food?

4. What trick did Jack want to play on Gran Val?

5. Did the trick go well? Why?

Find the words to fill the gaps.

1. A _____ was by her feet.   (page 2)

2. The _____ is a treat.   (page 5)

3. _____ give me the creeps.   (page 8)

What's missing?

1. it was tashas   (page 2)

2. i hate cats said gran val   (page 4)

3. ive got a good trick to play on gran   (page 10)

*Put the **verbs** (peeped, screams, seen) in the right gaps.*

1. I've _____ a stray cat.   (page 3)

2. Even Jack _____ at them.   (page 8)

3. The cat's face _____ out.   (page 9)

Which word in the story means

1. lost or homeless?   (page 3)

2. chicken or beef?   (page 3)

3. looked or peered?   (page 9)

4. joke or prank?   (page 10)

*Swap the word in **bold** for a new word that means the opposite.*

5. I **hate** cats.

6. This rat was **real**.